Wendy Cope
Family Values

Walter de la Mare
Selected Poems
Edited by Matthew Sweeney
ff Poetry

Lawrence Durrell
Selected Poems
Edited by Peter Porter

James Fenton
Yellow Tulips
Poems 1968–2011
ff

David Harsent
Night

Michael Hofmann
Selected Poems
ff Poetry

Mick Imlah
The Lost Leader

Emma Jones
The Striped World

G000294220

Paul Muldoon
Maggot

Daljit Nagra
Tippoo Sultan's Incredible White-Man-Eating Tiger Toy-Machine!!!
ff

Alice Oswald
Memorial
ff Poetry

Don Paterson
Rain
ff

Chapcott
Of Mutability

Stephen Spender
New Collected Poems
ff Poetry

Derek Walcott
White Egrets

Hugo Williams
West End Final
ff

This diary belongs to

....

First published in 2023
by Faber & Faber Ltd
The Bindery
51 Hatton Garden
London EC1N 8HN

Designed and typeset by Faber & Faber Ltd
Printed in Turkey

Clauses in the Banking and Financial Dealings Act allow the government to alter dates at short notice

A CIP record for this book is available from the British Library

ISBN 978–0–571–37973–6

Faber & Faber Poetry Diary 2024

Faber & Faber was founded in 1929 ...

... but its roots go back further to the Scientific Press, which started publishing in the early years of the century. The press's largest shareholders were Sir Maurice and Lady Gwyer, and their desire to expand into general publishing led them to Geoffrey Faber, a fellow of All Souls College, Oxford. Faber and Gwyer was founded in 1925. After four years Faber took the company forward alone, and the story goes that Walter de la Mare suggested adding a second, fictitious Faber to balance the company name.

In the meantime, the firm had prospered. T. S. Eliot, who had been suggested to Geoffrey Faber by a colleague at All Souls, had left Lloyds Bank in London to join him as a director, and in its first season the firm issued Eliot's *Poems 1909–1925*. In addition, the catalogues from the early years included books by Jean Cocteau, Herbert Read and Vita Sackville-West.

Poetry was always to be a significant element in the list and under Eliot's aegis Marianne Moore, Louis MacNeice and David Jones soon joined Ezra Pound, W. H. Auden, Stephen Spender, James Joyce, Siegfried Sassoon, D. H. Lawrence and Walter de la Mare.

Under Geoffrey Faber's chairmanship the board in 1929 included Eliot, Richard de la Mare, Charles Stewart and Frank Morley. This young team built up a comprehensive and profitable catalogue distinguished by modern design, much of which is still in print. Biographies, memoirs, fiction, poetry, political and religious essays, art and architecture monographs, children's books and a pioneering range of ecology titles contributed towards an eclectic list full of character. Faber also produced Eliot's groundbreaking literary review *The Criterion*.

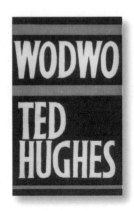

The Second World War brought both paper shortages and higher taxes, and the post-war years continued to be difficult. However, as the economy recovered a new generation of writers joined Faber, including William Golding, Robert Lowell, Ted Hughes, Sylvia Plath, Seamus Heaney, Philip Larkin, Thom Gunn and P. D. James. The publishing of Samuel Beckett and John Osborne began the firm's commitment to a modern drama list that now includes Tom Stoppard, Harold Pinter and David Hare.

Beginning in the 1970s, there was a blossoming in literary fiction, with the addition of authors such as Anna Burns, Peter Carey, Kazuo Ishiguro, Barbara Kingsolver, Mario Vargas Llosa and Orhan Pamuk.

The year 2024 finds the publishing company that Geoffrey Faber founded remaining true to the principles he instigated and independent of corporate ownership. In over ninety years of publishing, Faber & Faber can count among its authors seven Carnegie Medal winners, four Kate Greenaway Medal winners, more than twenty Whitbread/Costa Book Award winners, seven Booker Prize winners, twelve Forward Poetry Prize winners, and thirteen Nobel Laureates.

In addition to dedicated core publishing, recent years have seen some new strands emerge, including a distinctive Faber Audio list, the Faber Academy writing school and a Faber Members programme.

A more detailed chronology of Faber & Faber's poetry publishing appears at the back of this diary.

JANUARY

M	T	W	T	F	S	S
1	2	3	4	5	6	7
8	9	10	11	12	13	14
15	16	17	18	19	20	21
22	23	24	25	26	27	28
29	30	31	1	2	3	4
5	6	7	8	9	10	11

FEBRUARY

M	T	W	T	F	S	S
29	30	31	1	2	3	4
5	6	7	8	9	10	11
12	13	14	15	16	17	18
19	20	21	22	23	24	25
26	27	28	29	1	2	3
4	5	6	7	8	9	10

MARCH

M	T	W	T	F	S	S
26	27	28	29	1	2	3
4	5	6	7	8	9	10
11	12	13	14	15	16	17
18	19	20	21	22	23	24
25	26	27	28	29	30	31
1	2	3	4	5	6	7

APRIL

M	T	W	T	F	S	S
1	2	3	4	5	6	7
8	9	10	11	12	13	14
15	16	17	18	19	20	21
22	23	24	25	26	27	28
29	30	1	2	3	4	5
6	7	8	9	10	11	12

MAY

M	T	W	T	F	S	S
29	30	1	2	3	4	5
6	7	8	9	10	11	12
13	14	15	16	17	18	19
20	21	22	23	24	25	26
27	28	29	30	31	1	2
3	4	5	6	7	8	9

JUNE

M	T	W	T	F	S	S
27	28	29	30	31	1	2
3	4	5	6	7	8	9
10	11	12	13	14	15	16
17	18	19	20	21	22	23
24	25	26	27	28	29	30
1	2	3	4	5	6	7

JULY

M	T	W	T	F	S	S
1	2	3	4	5	6	7
8	9	10	11	12	13	14
15	16	17	18	19	20	21
22	23	24	25	26	27	28
29	30	31	1	2	3	4
5	6	7	8	9	10	11

AUGUST

M	T	W	T	F	S	S
29	30	31	1	2	3	4
5	6	7	8	9	10	11
12	13	14	15	16	17	18
19	20	21	22	23	24	25
26	27	28	29	30	31	1
2	3	4	5	6	7	8

SEPTEMBER

M	T	W	T	F	S	S
26	27	28	29	30	31	1
2	3	4	5	6	7	8
9	10	11	12	13	14	15
16	17	18	19	20	21	22
23	24	25	26	27	28	29
30	1	2	3	4	5	6

OCTOBER

M	T	W	T	F	S	S
30	1	2	3	4	5	6
7	8	9	10	11	12	13
14	15	16	17	18	19	20
21	22	23	24	25	26	27
28	29	30	31	1	2	3
4	5	6	7	8	9	10

NOVEMBER

M	T	W	T	F	S	S
28	29	30	31	1	2	3
4	5	6	7	8	9	10
11	12	13	14	15	16	17
18	19	20	21	22	23	24
25	26	27	28	29	30	1
2	3	4	5	6	7	8

DECEMBER

M	T	W	T	F	S	S
25	26	27	28	29	30	1
2	3	4	5	6	7	8
9	10	11	12	13	14	15
16	17	18	19	20	21	22
23	24	25	26	27	28	29
30	31	1	2	3	4	5

JANUARY

M	T	W	T	F	S	S
26	27	28	29	30	31	1
2	3	4	5	6	7	8
9	10	11	12	13	14	15
16	17	18	19	20	21	22
23	24	25	26	27	28	29
30	31	1	2	3	4	5

FEBRUARY

M	T	W	T	F	S	S
30	31	1	2	3	4	5
6	7	8	9	10	11	12
13	14	15	16	17	18	19
20	21	22	23	24	25	26
27	28	1	2	3	4	5
6	7	8	9	10	11	12

MARCH

M	T	W	T	F	S	S
27	28	1	2	3	4	5
6	7	8	9	10	11	12
13	14	15	16	17	18	19
20	21	22	23	24	25	26
27	28	29	30	31	1	2
3	4	5	6	7	8	9

APRIL

M	T	W	T	F	S	S
27	28	29	30	31	1	2
3	4	5	6	7	8	9
10	11	12	13	14	15	16
17	18	19	20	21	22	23
24	25	26	27	28	29	30
1	2	3	4	5	6	7

MAY

M	T	W	T	F	S	S
1	2	3	4	5	6	7
8	9	10	11	12	13	14
15	16	17	18	19	20	21
22	23	24	25	26	27	28
29	30	31	1	2	3	4
5	6	7	8	9	10	11

JUNE

M	T	W	T	F	S	S
29	30	31	1	2	3	4
5	6	7	8	9	10	11
12	13	14	15	16	17	18
19	20	21	22	23	24	25
26	27	28	29	30	1	2
3	4	5	6	7	8	9

JULY

M	T	W	T	F	S	S
26	27	28	29	30	1	2
3	4	5	6	7	8	9
10	11	12	13	14	15	16
17	18	19	20	21	22	23
24	25	26	27	28	29	30
31	1	2	3	4	5	6

AUGUST

M	T	W	T	F	S	S
31	1	2	3	4	5	6
7	8	9	10	11	12	13
14	15	16	17	18	19	20
21	22	23	24	25	26	27
28	29	30	31	1	2	3
4	5	6	7	8	9	10

SEPTEMBER

M	T	W	T	F	S	S
28	29	30	31	1	2	3
4	5	6	7	8	9	10
11	12	13	14	15	16	17
18	19	20	21	22	23	24
25	26	27	28	29	30	1
2	3	4	5	6	7	8

OCTOBER

M	T	W	T	F	S	S
25	26	27	28	29	30	1
2	3	4	5	6	7	8
9	10	11	12	13	14	15
16	17	18	19	20	21	22
23	24	25	26	27	28	29
30	31	1	2	3	4	5

NOVEMBER

M	T	W	T	F	S	S
30	31	1	2	3	4	5
6	7	8	9	10	11	12
13	14	15	16	17	18	19
20	21	22	23	24	25	26
27	28	29	30	1	2	3
4	5	6	7	8	9	10

DECEMBER

M	T	W	T	F	S	S
27	28	29	30	1	2	3
4	5	6	7	8	9	10
11	12	13	14	15	16	17
18	19	20	21	22	23	24
25	26	27	28	29	30	31
1	2	3	4	5	6	7

JANUARY

M	T	W	T	F	S	S
30	31	1	2	3	4	5
6	7	8	9	10	11	12
13	14	15	16	17	18	19
20	21	22	23	24	25	26
27	28	29	30	31	1	2
3	4	5	6	7	8	9

FEBRUARY

M	T	W	T	F	S	S
27	28	29	30	31	1	2
3	4	5	6	7	8	9
10	11	12	13	14	15	16
17	18	19	20	21	22	23
24	25	26	27	28	1	2
3	4	5	6	7	8	9

MARCH

M	T	W	T	F	S	S
24	25	26	27	28	1	2
3	4	5	6	7	8	9
10	11	12	13	14	15	16
17	18	19	20	21	22	23
24	25	26	27	28	29	30
31	1	2	3	4	5	6

APRIL

M	T	W	T	F	S	S
31	1	2	3	4	5	6
7	8	9	10	11	12	13
14	15	16	17	18	19	20
21	22	23	24	25	26	27
28	29	30	1	2	3	4
5	6	7	8	9	10	11

MAY

M	T	W	T	F	S	S
28	29	30	1	2	3	4
5	6	7	8	9	10	11
12	13	14	15	16	17	18
19	20	21	22	23	24	25
26	27	28	29	30	31	1
2	3	4	5	6	7	8

JUNE

M	T	W	T	F	S	S
26	27	28	29	30	31	1
2	3	4	5	6	7	8
9	10	11	12	13	14	15
16	17	18	19	20	21	22
23	24	25	26	27	28	29
30	1	2	3	4	5	6

JULY

M	T	W	T	F	S	S
30	1	2	3	4	5	6
7	8	9	10	11	12	13
14	15	16	17	18	19	20
21	22	23	24	25	26	27
28	29	30	31	1	2	3
4	5	6	7	8	9	10

AUGUST

M	T	W	T	F	S	S
28	29	30	31	1	2	3
4	5	6	7	8	9	10
11	12	13	14	15	16	17
18	19	20	21	22	23	24
25	26	27	28	29	30	31
1	2	3	4	5	6	7

SEPTEMBER

M	T	W	T	F	S	S
1	2	3	4	5	6	7
8	9	10	11	12	13	14
15	16	17	18	19	20	21
22	23	24	25	26	27	28
29	30	1	2	3	4	5
6	7	8	9	10	11	12

OCTOBER

M	T	W	T	F	S	S
29	30	1	2	3	4	5
6	7	8	9	10	11	12
13	14	15	16	17	18	19
20	21	22	23	24	25	26
27	28	29	30	31	1	2
3	4	5	6	7	8	9

NOVEMBER

M	T	W	T	F	S	S
27	28	29	30	31	1	2
3	4	5	6	7	8	9
10	11	12	13	14	15	16
17	18	19	20	21	22	23
24	25	26	27	28	29	30
1	2	3	4	5	6	7

DECEMBER

M	T	W	T	F	S	S
1	2	3	4	5	6	7
8	9	10	11	12	13	14
15	16	17	18	19	20	21
22	23	24	25	26	27	28
29	30	31	1	2	3	4
5	6	7	8	9	10	11

Nick
Laird

Go
Giants

Poetry

ff

1 Monday NEW YEAR'S DAY

2 Tuesday 2ND JANUARY HOLIDAY (SCT)
DAY AFTER NEW YEAR'S DAY (NZ)

3 Wednesday

4 Thursday

5 Friday

6 Saturday

7 Sunday

from Glanmore Revisited

VII The Skylight

You were the one for skylights. I opposed
Cutting into the seasoned tongue-and-groove
Of pitch pine. I liked it low and closed,
Its claustrophobic, nest-up-in-the-roof
Effect. I liked the snuff-dry feeling,
The perfect, trunk-lid fit of the old ceiling.
Under there, it was all hutch and hatch.
The blue slates kept the heat like midnight thatch.

But when the slates came off, extravagant
Sky entered and held surprise wide open.
For days I felt like an inhabitant
Of that house where the man sick of the palsy
Was lowered through the roof, had his sins forgiven,
Was healed, took up his bed and walked away.

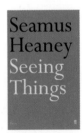

Seamus
Heaney
Seeing
Things

Seeing Things (1991)

8 Monday

9 Tuesday

10 Wednesday

11 Thursday

12 Friday

13 Saturday 14 Sunday

Sheep in Fog

The hills step off into whiteness.
People or stars
Regard me sadly, I disappoint them.

The train leaves a line of breath.
O slow
Horse the color of rust,

Hooves, dolorous bells——
All morning the
Morning has been blackening,

A flower left out.
My bones hold a stillness, the far
Fields melt my heart.

They threaten
To let me through to a heaven
Starless and fatherless, a dark water.

Sylvia Plath Poems Chosen by Carol Ann Duffy (2012)

15 Monday

16 Tuesday

17 Wednesday

18 Thursday

19 Friday

20 Saturday   21 Sunday

Hadrian's Wall

Around the old blown names
Birdoswald, Cawfields or Vindolanda,
each fortress and straight line of stone
partition was built by a zealous emperor
to keep out the barbarous.

I've come to this wall crowning England,
this symbol of divided man,
to honour the lineage of our tall ideals;
to ask, the more stacked, the more shielded
a haven, the cleaner the stock?

Where will our walls finally end? In
the gigabytes of our biometric online
lives, in our passports? To keep us
from trespass, will our walls be raised
watchful as the Great Firewall of China?

Daljit
Nagra
British
Museum

British Museum (2017)

22 Monday

23 Tuesday

24 Wednesday

25 Thursday   BURNS NIGHT

26 Friday   AUSTRALIA DAY (AUS)

27 Saturday   28 Sunday

(It was as if I were asleep)

It was as if I were asleep the whole of my life
and I didn't know a thing, nothing on the
inside, not that life was life, or death is death,
how I was right or how I was wrong, that
nothing lasts and there's no one to blame, and
nobody gets out of it, not even you, not even
me, nobody gets out of it alive, but as long as
I live, come to me, as long as my love has the
strength of the blood that gives life and the
grief of the blood that drains away, come to
me wired and wild like the bare tree and the
shedding sky . . .

after Mary Oliver
& Tina Turner

Unexhausted Time (2022)

29 Monday

30 Tuesday

31 Wednesday

1 Thursday

2 Friday

3 Saturday   4 Sunday

On Wenlock Edge

On Wenlock Edge the wood's in trouble;
His forest fleece the Wrekin heaves;
The gale, it plies the saplings double,
And thick on Severn snow the leaves.

'Twould blow like this through hold and hangar
When Uricon the city stood:
'Tis the old wind in the old anger,
But then it threshed another wood.

Then, 'twas before my time, the Roman
At yonder, heaving hill would stare:
The blood that warms an English yeoman,
The thoughts that hurt him, they were there.

There, like the wind through woods in riot,
Through him the gale of life blew high;
The tree of man was never quiet:
Then 'twas the Roman, now 'tis I.

The gale, it plies the saplings double,
It blows so hard, 'twill soon be gone:
Today the Roman and his trouble
Are ashes under Uricon.

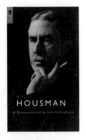

POET TO POET *A. E. Housman: Poems Selected by Alan Hollinghurst* (2005)

5 Monday

6 Tuesday   WAITANGI DAY (NZ)

7 Wednesday

8 Thursday

9 Friday

10 Saturday   11 Sunday

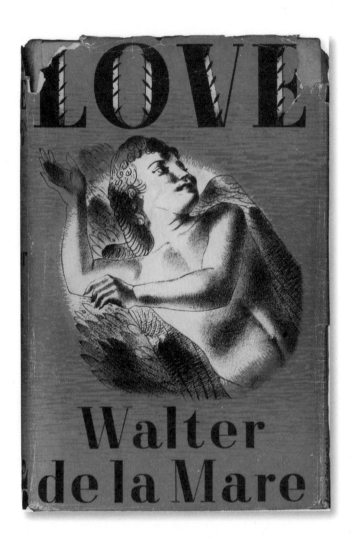

12 Monday

13 Tuesday

14 Wednesday   VALENTINE'S DAY

15 Thursday

16 Friday

17 Saturday

18 Sunday

Heart for Sale

twilight quarter
backstreet corner
junk shop window
good working order

heart for sale
open to offers
throw in a soul
one careless owner

family heirloom
formaldehyde perfume
drop the grenade, son
let bygones be bygones

heart for sale
open to offers
throw in a soul
one careless owner

weasels they say
can wheedle their way
through eternity rings
and wormholes in space

heart for sale
open to offers
throw in a soul
one careless owner

Never Good with Horses (2023)

19 Monday

20 Tuesday

21 Wednesday

22 Thursday

23 Friday

24 Saturday

25 Sunday

I Am

I am – yet what I am, none cares or knows;
    My friends forsake me like a memory lost: –
I am the self-consumer of my woes; –
    They rise and vanish in oblivion's host,
Like shadows in love's frenzied stifled throes: –
And yet I am, and live – like vapours tost

Into the nothingness of scorn and noise, –
    Into the living sea of waking dreams,
Where there is neither sense of life or joys,
    But the vast shipwreck of my life's esteems;
Even the dearest, that I love the best
Are strange – nay, rather stranger than the rest.

I long for scenes, where man hath never trod
    A place where woman never smiled or wept
There to abide with my Creator, God;
    And sleep as I in childhood, sweetly slept,
Untroubling, and untroubled where I lie,
The grass below – above, the vaulted sky.

POET TO POET *John Clare: Poems Selected by Paul Farley* (2016)

26 Monday

27 Tuesday

28 Wednesday

29 Thursday

1 Friday   ST DAVID'S DAY

2 Saturday   3 Sunday

Gwawrddur [99]

Ef gwant tra thrichant echasaf,
Ef lladdai a pherfedd ac eithaf,
Oedd gwiw ym mlaen llu llariaf,
Goddolai o haid meirch y gaeaf.
Gochorai brain du ar fur caer
Cyn ni bai ef Arthur.
Rhwng cyfnerthi yng nghlysur,
Yng nghwnnor, gwernor Gwawrddur.

*

Charging ahead of the three hundred
he cut down the centre and the wing.

Blazing ahead of the finest army,
he gave horses from his winter herd.

He fed ravens on the fortress wall
though he was no Arthur.

Among the strongest in the war,
Gwawrddur, citadel.

The Gododdin (2021)

4 Monday

5 Tuesday

6 Wednesday

7 Thursday

8 Friday

9 Saturday   10 Sunday

from Landscapes III

Usk

Do not suddenly break the branch, or
Hope to find
The white hart behind the white well.
Glance aside, not for lance, do not spell
Old enchantments. Let them sleep.
'Gently dip, but not too deep',
Lift your eyes
Where the roads dip and where the roads rise
Seek only there
Where the grey light meets the green air
The hermit's chapel, the pilgrim's prayer.

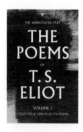

11 Monday

12 Tuesday

13 Wednesday

14 Thursday

15 Friday

16 Saturday

17 Sunday ST PATRICK'S DAY (NI, IRL)

SOLSTICES

LOUIS MAC- NEICE

POEMS

18 Monday

19 Tuesday

20 Wednesday

21 Thursday HUMAN RIGHTS DAY (ZA)

22 Friday

23 Saturday   24 Sunday

The Pan

When he stopped at last in the long main street
Of the small town, after that hundred
And ninety miles, the five-o'clock, September,
Brassy, low, wet Westcountry sun
Above the street's far end, and when
He had extricated his stiffness
From the car crammed with books, carrier bags
Of crockery, cutlery and baby things,
And crossed the tilting street in that strange town
To buy a pan to heat milk and babyfood
The moment they arrived
Hours ahead of their furniture
Into their stripped new house, in their strange new life,
He did not notice that the ironmonger's
Where he bought the pan had been closed
And empty for two years. And returning
With the little pan he did not notice
A man on the pavement staring at him,
His arm round a young woman who wore
A next-to-nothing long evening dress
Slashed to the hip, and a white, silk, open-work shawl
Round her naked shoulders, and leopard-claw earrings,
He did not recognise, nor did his wife
As he squeezed back weary beside her
Behind the wheel of the Morris Traveller,
That this man, barely two yards from them,
Staring at them both so fixedly,
The man so infinitely more alive
Than either of them there in the happy car
Was himself – knowing their whole future
And helpless to warn them.

25 Monday

26 Tuesday

27 Wednesday

28 Thursday

29 Friday GOOD FRIDAY (UK, AUS, ZA, NZ)

30 Saturday EASTER (HOLY) SATURDAY

31 Sunday EASTER SUNDAY

There You Are

There you are
this cold day
boiling the water on the stove
pouring the herbs into the pot
hawthorn, rose;
buying the tulips
& looking at them, holding
your heart in your hands at the table
saying *please*, *please*, to nobody else
here in the kitchen with you.
How hard, how heavy this all is.
How beautiful, these things you do,
in case they help, these things you do
which, although you haven't said it yet,
say that you want to live.

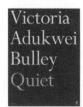

Quiet (2022)

1 Monday   EASTER MONDAY (UK, IRL, AUS, NZ)
                 FAMILY DAY (ZA)

2 Tuesday

3 Wednesday

4 Thursday

5 Friday

6 Saturday   7 Sunday

To a Lady with 'The Temple of Fame'

What's Fame with Men, by Custom of the Nation,
Is call'd in Women only Reputation:
About them both why keep we such a pother?
Part you with one, and I'll renounce the other.

The Funny Side (2012)

8 Monday

9 Tuesday

10 Wednesday

11 Thursday

12 Friday

13 Saturday   14 Sunday

Count That Day Lost

If you sit down at set of sun
And count the acts that you have done,
And, counting, find
One self-denying deed, one word
That eased the heart of him who heard,
One glance most kind
That fell like sunshine where it went —
Then you may count that day well spent.

But if, through all the livelong day,
You've cheered no heart, by yea or nay —
If, through it all
You've nothing done that you can trace
That brought the sunshine to one face —
No act most small
That helped some soul and nothing cost —
Then count that day as worse than lost.

Winning Words (2012)

15 Monday

16 Tuesday

17 Wednesday

18 Thursday

19 Friday

20 Saturday   21 Sunday

Foxglove Country

Sometimes I like to hide in the word
foxgloves – in the middle of *foxgloves*.
The *xgl* is hard to say, out of the England
of its harbouring word.
Alone it becomes a small tangle,
a witch's thimble, hard-to-toll bell,
elvish door to a door. *Xgl*
a place with a locked beginning
then a snag, a *gl*
like the little Englands of my grief,
a knotted dark that locks light
in *glisten*, *glow*, *glint*, *gleam*
and Oberon's banks of *eglantine*
which closes in on the opening
of *Gulliver* whose shrunken *gul*
says 'rose' in my fatherland.
Meanwhile, in the motherland, the *xg*
is almost the thumb of a lost mitten,
an impossible interior, deeper than forests
and further in. And deeper inland
is the gulp, the gulf, the gap, the grip
that goes before *love*.

England's Green (2022)

22 Monday

23 Tuesday   ST GEORGE'S DAY

24 Wednesday

25 Thursday   ANZAC DAY (AUS, NZ)

26 Friday

27 Saturday   FREEDOM DAY (ZA)   28 Sunday

The Question

When did you know you wanted to become
A poet? No one believes this question.
No one listens for the answer. It's one
Of those habits of people forced to live
Together on a spinning rock, the pale
Blue dot a wince in the wide attention
The dying light seeks out from ice giants
Dull and firm in the dark, under polite
Lights, midst rows and rows of people who ask
When and why about poetry, of she
Who forgets to ask something that was,
I realize later, part of the poem,
The part where it all comes together, and,
Having come together, finally sings.

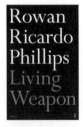

Living Weapon (2021)

29 Monday

30 Tuesday

1 Wednesday   WORKERS' DAY (ZA)

2 Thursday

3 Friday

4 Saturday   5 Sunday

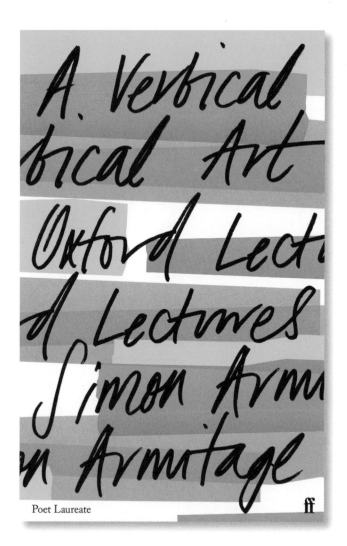

Poet Laureate

6 Monday   EARLY MAY BANK HOLIDAY (UK)
MAY DAY (IRL)

7 Tuesday

8 Wednesday

9 Thursday

10 Friday

11 Saturday   12 Sunday

North European

Novels with characters
who don't have roomy
nineteenth-century selves.

Novels for people who don't have
roomy
nineteenth-century lives.

Novels for people who are stretched thin.
A clean modern apartment
glass metal minimalist.

Solitudes.
Bewildering passions
today, long ago.

For preference bicycles.
Underfoot in the ice months
ice crinkles.

The Missing Months (2022)

13 Monday

14 Tuesday

15 Wednesday

16 Thursday

17 Friday

18 Saturday

19 Sunday

Talking in Bed

Talking in bed ought to be easiest,
Lying together there goes back so far,
An emblem of two people being honest.

Yet more and more time passes silently.
Outside, the wind's incomplete unrest
Builds and disperses clouds about the sky,

And dark towns heap up on the horizon.
None of this cares for us. Nothing shows why
At this unique distance from isolation

It becomes still more difficult to find
Words at once true and kind,
Or not untrue and not unkind.

The Complete Poems (2012)

20 Monday

21 Tuesday

22 Wednesday

23 Thursday

24 Friday

25 Saturday   26 Sunday

The Wayfarers

Is it the hour? We leave this resting-place
    Made fair by one another for a while.
Now, for a god-speed, one last mad embrace;
    The long road then, unlit by your faint smile.
Ah! the long road! and you so far away!
Oh, I'll remember! but . . . each crawling day
    Will pale a little your scarlet lips, each mile
Dull the dear pain of your remembered face.

. . . Do you think there's a far border town,
    somewhere,
    The desert's edge, last of the lands we know,
    Some gaunt eventual limit of our light,
    In which I'll find you waiting; and we'll go
Together, hand in hand again, out there,
    Into the waste we know not, into the night?

Rupert Brooke: The Poetical Works edited by Geoffrey Keynes (2014)

27 **Monday**   SPRING BANK HOLIDAY (UK)

28 Tuesday

29 Wednesday

30 Thursday

31 Friday

1 Saturday   2 Sunday

Pippa's Song

The year's at the spring
And day's at the morn;
Morning's at seven;
The hill-side's dew-pearled;
The lark's on the wing;
The snail's on the thorn:
God's in his heaven –
All's right with the world!

POET TO POET *Robert Browning: Poems Selected by Douglas Dunn* (2004)

3 Monday KING'S BIRTHDAY HOLIDAY (NZ)

4 Tuesday

5 Wednesday

6 Thursday

7 Friday

8 Saturday   9 Sunday

He Wishes for the Cloths of Heaven

Had I the heavens' embroidered cloths,
Enwrought with golden and silver light,
The blue and the dim and the dark cloths
Of night and light and the half-light,
I would spread the cloths under your feet:
But I, being poor, have only my dreams;
I have spread my dreams under your feet;
Tread softly because you tread on my dreams.

POET TO POET *W. B. Yeats: Poems Selected by Seamus Heaney* (2009)

10 Monday

11 Tuesday

12 Wednesday

13 Thursday

14 Friday

15 Saturday

16 Sunday   YOUTH DAY (ZA)

W. H. Auden
Collected
Poems

edited by Edward Mendelson

Poetry

ff

17 **Monday**   YOUTH DAY HOLIDAY (ZA)

18 Tuesday

19 Wednesday

20 Thursday

21 Friday

22 Saturday   23 Sunday

Say not the struggle nought availeth

Say not the struggle nought availeth,
  The labour and the wounds are vain,
The enemy faints not, nor faileth,
  And as things have been, things remain.

If hopes were dupes, fears may be liars;
  It may be, in yon smoke concealed,
Your comrades chase e'en now the fliers,
  And, but for you, possess the field.

For while the tired waves, vainly breaking,
  Seem here no painful inch to gain,
Far back through creeks and inlets making
  Comes, silent, flooding in, the main,

And not by eastern windows only,
  When daylight comes, comes in the light,
In front the sun climbs slow, how slowly,
  But westward, look, the land is bright.

Winning Words (2012)

24 Monday

25 Tuesday

26 Wednesday

27 Thursday

28 Friday

29 Saturday   30 Sunday

There came a Wind like a Bugle –

There came a Wind like a Bugle –
It quivered through the Grass
And a Green Chill upon the Heat
So ominous did pass
We barred the Windows and the Doors
As from an Emerald Ghost –
The Doom's electric Moccasin
That very instant passed –
On a strange Mob of panting Trees
and Fences fled away
And Rivers where the Houses ran
Those looked that lived – that Day –
The Bell within the steeple wild
The flying tidings told –
How much can come
And much can go,
And yet abide the World!

POET TO POET *Emily Dickinson: Poems Selected by Ted Hughes* (2004)

1 Monday

2 Tuesday

3 Wednesday

4 Thursday

5 Friday

6 Saturday

7 Sunday

Mere

for John Barnie

Today the mere turns a blind eye to the white overhead,
but when the wind gets up it shivers in its sequins.

There is blue in the bands around the stem of the dragonfly,
a few tatters of sunlight in the flowers of the yellow flag.

A heron mimes a pond ornament in the shallows,
as a mallard takes off from its runway of splashes.

The air above the bulrushes is granular with midges.
On the surface a pond-skater pilots a flotilla of dimples.

The metallic swivelling of roaches is no guide.
Following those arrows will get you nowhere.

There's a green finer than we can see, the hydra budding its
    offspring.
Another mere laps within the cell wall of the amoeba.

Wing (2020)

8 Monday

9 Tuesday

10 Wednesday

11 Thursday

12 Friday   BATTLE OF THE BOYNE (NI)

13 Saturday   14 Sunday

The Visionary

Silent is the house: all are laid asleep:
One alone looks out o'er the snow-wreaths deep,
Watching every cloud, dreading every breeze
That whirls the wildering drift, and bends the groaning trees.

Cheerful is the hearth, soft the matted floor;
Not one shivering gust creeps through pane or door;
The little lamp burns straight, its rays shoot strong and far:
I trim it well, to be the wanderer's guiding-star.

Frown, my haughty sire! chide, my angry dame;
Set your slaves to spy; threaten me with shame:
But neither sire nor dame, nor prying serf shall know,
What angel nightly tracks that waste of frozen snow.

What I love shall come like visitant of air,
Safe in secret power from lurking human snare;
What loves me, no word of mine shall e'er betray,
Though for faith unstained my life must forfeit pay.

The Map and the Clock: Poetry of Britain and Ireland Chosen by Carol Ann Duffy and Gillian Clarke (2016)

15 Monday

16 Tuesday

17 Wednesday

18 Thursday

19 Friday

20 Saturday 21 Sunday

By the River

The day is so still
you can almost hear the heat.
You can almost hear
that royal blue dragonfly
landing on the old white boat.

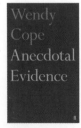

Anecdotal Evidence (2018)

22 Monday

23 Tuesday

24 Wednesday

25 Thursday

26 Friday

27 Saturday   28 Sunday

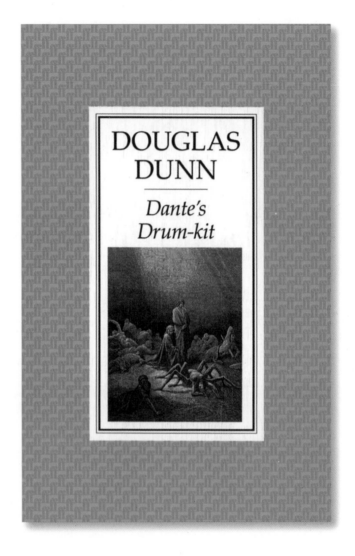

DOUGLAS
DUNN

*Dante's
Drum-kit*

29 Monday

30 Tuesday

31 Wednesday

1 Thursday

2 Friday

3 Saturday

4 Sunday

The Shade-Catchers

I think they were about as high
As haycocks are. They went running by
Catching bits of shade in the sunny street:
'I've got one,' cried sister to brother.
    'I've got two.' 'Now I've got another.'
But scudding away on their little bare feet,
They left the shade in the sunny street.

Selected Poetry and Prose edited by Julia Copus (2019)

5 Monday   AUGUST BANK HOLIDAY (SCT, IRL)

6 Tuesday

7 Wednesday

8 Thursday

9 Friday   NATIONAL WOMEN'S DAY (ZA)

10 Saturday   11 Sunday

Ah! Sunflower

Ah, Sunflower! weary of time,
Who countest the steps of the Sun,
Seeking after that sweet golden clime
Where the traveller's journey is done:

Where the Youth pined away with desire,
And the pale Virgin shrouded in snow
Arise from their graves, and aspire
Where my Sunflower wishes to go.

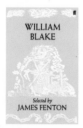

POET TO POET   *William Blake: Poems Selected by James Fenton* (2010)

12 Monday

13 Tuesday

14 Wednesday

15 Thursday

16 Friday

17 Saturday

18 Sunday

The fishermen rowing homeward . . .

The fishermen rowing homeward in the dusk,
Do not consider the stillness through which they move.
So I since feelings drown, should no more ask
What twilight and safety your strong hands gave.
And the night, urger of the old lies
Winked at by stars that sentry the humped hills,
Should hear no words of faring forth, for time knows
That bitter and sly sea, and love raises walls.

Yet others, who now watch my progress outward
To a sea which is crueler than any word
Of love, may see in me the calm my voyage makes,
Parting new water in the antique hoax.
And the secure from thinking may climb safe to liners,
Hearing small rumors of paddlers drowned near stars.

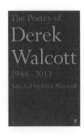

The Poetry of Derek Walcott 1948–2013 Selected by Glyn Maxwell (2014)

19 Monday

20 Tuesday

21 Wednesday

22 Thursday

23 Friday

24 Saturday

25 Sunday

Dayroom

She sits by herself in the dayroom, tracing the wallflowers
on her towelling peignoir, petals . . . stem,
and runs through all the things she will not tell him:
the marriage bed they stripped and dressed for the birth,
the mounting pain, the tarry scent of Lysol . . .

Because he has asked her please not to spare any details
and nothing, she knows, would gladden him more than to picture
the way her hair stuck damply to her temples
and hung in ribbony strands, her blood-streaked thighs
like two sleek seals exhausted from the journey;

or to hear how the telephone rang at just the wrong moment
and the way her husband hurried at once to answer
and how all this accounts for the death of the baby;
because it would help him, because it would please him no end
to gather the bits from her like fine bone china

so damaged he alone could piece them together
and to set it all down in his fluent, looping hand,
she shuts the lot inside her, where it gleams
as treasure will do, lowered into the ground,
deep, then deeper down, for no one to find.

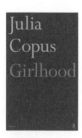

Girlhood (2019)

26 **Monday**   SUMMER BANK HOLIDAY (UK)

27 Tuesday

28 Wednesday

29 Thursday

30 Friday

31 Saturday   1 Sunday

The Black Cloud

Little flocks of peaceful clouds,
    Lying in your fields so blue,
While my eyes look up they see
    A black Ram coming close to you.

He will scatter you poor flocks,
    He will tear up north and south;
Lightning will come from his eye,
    And fierce thunder from his mouth.

Little flocks of peaceful clouds,
    Soon there'll be a dreadful rout;
That Ram's horns can toss big ships,
    Tear an oak tree's bowels out.

The Rattle Bag (2005)

2 Monday

3 Tuesday

4 Wednesday

5 Thursday

6 Friday

7 Saturday   8 Sunday

The Sense of Movement

Thom Gunn

FABER paper covered EDITIONS

9 Monday

10 Tuesday

11 Wednesday

12 Thursday

13 Friday

14 Saturday   15 Sunday

I saw a Peacock with a fiery tail

I saw a Peacock with a fiery tail
I saw a blazing Comet drop down hail
I saw a Cloud with Ivy circled round
I saw a sturdy Oak creep on the ground
I saw a Pismire swallow up a Whale
I saw a raging Sea brim full of Ale
I saw a Venice Glass sixteen foot deep
I saw a Well full of men's tears that weep
I saw their Eyes all in a flame of fire
I saw a House as big as the Moon and higher
I saw the Sun even in the midst of night
I saw the Man that saw this wondrous sight.

Winning Words (2012)

16 Monday

17 Tuesday

18 Wednesday

19 Thursday

20 Friday

21 Saturday   22 Sunday

Conversation with Fantasy Mother

Dear fantasy mother, thank you
for taking my coming out as calmly
as a pond accepts a stone
flung into its depths.

You sieved my tears, added
an egg, then baked a beautiful cake.
You said: *Let us celebrate, for today
you are reborn as my beloved.*

The candles gleamed and the icing
was almost true – impossibly white –
coated with the sweetness of
sprinkles. We sat together

at the table and ate. Afterwards,
I returned to my room and touched
all the forbidden parts of myself, felt
a kindness I had not known in years.

Flèche (2019)

23 Monday

24 Tuesday   HERITAGE DAY (ZA)

25 Wednesday

26 Thursday

27 Friday

28 Saturday   29 Sunday

A Toast

October: grapes hung like the fists of a girl
gassed in her prayer. *Memory*,
I whisper, *stay awake*.

In my veins
long syllables tighten their ropes, rains come
right out of the eighteenth century
Yiddish or a darker language in which imagination
is the only word.

Imagination! a young girl dancing polka,
unafraid, betrayed by the Lord's death
(or his hiding under the bed when the Messiah
was postponed).

In my country, evenings bring the rainwater, turning
poplars bronze in a light that sparkles on these pages
where I, my fathers,
unable to describe your dreams, drink
my silence from a cup.

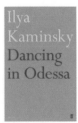

Dancing in Odessa (2021)

30 Monday

1 Tuesday

2 Wednesday

3 Thursday

4 Friday

5 Saturday

6 Sunday

The silver swan, who living had no note

The silver swan, who living had no note,
When death approached unlocked her silent throat;
Leaning her breast against the reedy shore,
Thus sung her first and last, and sung no more:
Farewell, all joys; O death, come close mine eyes;
More geese than swans now live, more fools than wise.

The Rattle Bag (2005)

7 Monday

8 Tuesday

9 Wednesday

10 Thursday

11 Friday

12 Saturday   13 Sunday

Fog

A photograph of the nineteen-fifties:
figures in fog.

Black and white, because it's post-war
and colour is rationed.

Also, that's all fog needs, a slightly
dirty white.

The figures, smudges of off-black,
blur into the fog.

They stand in an unfamiliar street,
perspective suspended.

Godlike, the fog has descended
to give each a hug.

But it's the opposite of Pentecost:
a freeze, a silence.

Fixed there, the figures, for all that,
are not lost.

This is the element in which they live;
where I lived, too.

Toys/Tricks/Traps (2023)

Christopher
Reid
Toys/Tricks/
Traps

14 Monday

15 Tuesday

16 Wednesday

17 Thursday

18 Friday

19 Saturday   20 Sunday

THE GODODDIN
LAMENT FOR THE FALLEN

A VERSION BY
Gillian Clarke

ff

21 Monday

22 Tuesday

23 Wednesday

24 Thursday

25 Friday

26 Saturday

27 Sunday

from God Complex

Seagulls underlit by sundown.
What's the point of all this text?
I still have to live without you.
I feel incandescent rage at people
who block ants' nests' swirls outside
their homes. What kind of god
complex is this? Let them live;
let them maul the house
and surfaces with black trail.

Rachael
Allen
God
Complex

God Complex (2024)

28 Monday   LABOUR DAY (NZ)
            OCTOBER BANK HOLIDAY (IRL)

29 Tuesday

30 Wednesday

31 Thursday   HALLOWEEN

1 Friday

2 Saturday   3 Sunday

Night crept up on them

Night crept up on them

black sleep closed their eyes

Short and Sweet (2002)

4 Monday

5 Tuesday

6 Wednesday

7 Thursday

8 Friday

9 Saturday

10 Sunday REMEMBRANCE SUNDAY

The Mud Sermon

They shovelled the long trenches day and night.

Frostbitten mud. Shellshock mud. Dungheap mud. Imperial mud.
Venereal mud. Malaria mud. Hun bait mud. Mating mud.
1655 mud: white flashes of sharks. Golgotha mud. Chilblain mud.
Caliban mud. Cannibal mud. Ha ha ha mud. Amnesia mud.
Drapetomania mud. Lice mud. Pyrexia mud. Exposure mud. Aphasia mud.
No-man's-land's-Everyman's mud. And the smoking flax mud.
Dysentery mud. Septic sore mud. Hog pen mud. Nephritis mud.
Constipated mud. Faith mud. Sandfly fever mud. Rat mud.
Sheol mud. Ir-ha-cheres mud. Ague mud. Asquith mud. Parade mud.
Scabies mud. Mumps mud. Memra mud. Pneumonia mud.
Mene Mene Tekel Upharsin mud. Civil war mud.
And darkness and worms will be their dwelling-place mud.
Yaws mud. Gog mud. Magog mud. God mud.
Canaan the unseen, as promised, saw mud.

They resurrected new counter-kingdoms,
by the arbitrament of the sword mud.

Ishion
Hutchinson
**School of
Instructions**

School of Instructions (2023)

11 Monday   REMEMBRANCE DAY

12 Tuesday

13 Wednesday

14 Thursday

15 Friday

16 Saturday   17 Sunday

A Winter Apple

for Nora Chassler

Here, I got you one of those you like:
those bewildered late bloomers, tough and small
and sweeter than they've any right to be,
as green as Eden, the red an afterthought
as if there'd been an hour left in the season
to paint them all, and where the brush had swept
the snow-white fruit below is stained with pink
as if your teeth had bled from biting it.
It was hard enough to body itself forth
with so few leaves to hide it from the frost
without it burning fuel on working out
where its skin stopped and its flesh began.
All that touched it shook its heart. It was that
or it was nothing. Take it in your pocket
on your long Sunday walk to eat by the loch
with that lone jackdaw only you can talk to.
I make no great claims for this little thing
but I promise only good will come of it.

The Arctic (2022)

18 Monday

---

19 Tuesday

---

20 Wednesday

---

21 Thursday

---

22 Friday

---

23 Saturday   24 Sunday

The Announcement

They came, the brothers, and took two chairs
    In their usual quiet way;
And for a time we did not think
    They had much to say.

And they began and talked awhile
    Of ordinary things,
Till spread that silence in the room
    A pent thought brings.

And then they said: 'The end has come.
    Yes: it has come at last.'
And we looked down, and knew that day
    A spirit had passed.

Short and Sweet (2002)

25 Monday

26 Tuesday

27 Wednesday

28 Thursday

29 Friday

30 Saturday   ST ANDREW'S DAY   1 Sunday

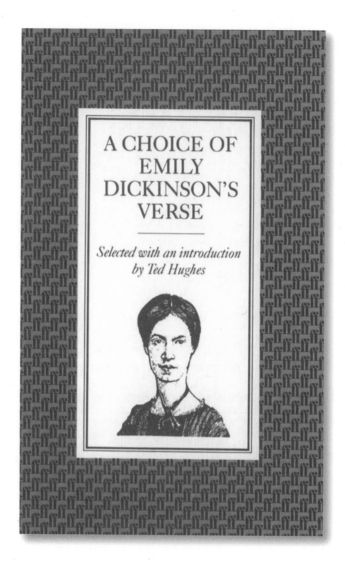

A CHOICE OF
EMILY
DICKINSON'S
VERSE

*Selected with an introduction
by Ted Hughes*

2 Monday ST ANDREW'S DAY HOLIDAY (SCT)

3 Tuesday

4 Wednesday

5 Thursday

6 Friday

7 Saturday   8 Sunday

The Watchers

By the ford at the town's edge
Horse and carter rest:
The carter smokes on the bridge
Watching the water press in swathes
    about his horse's chest.

From the inn one watches, too,
In the room for visitors
That has no fire, but a view
And many cases of stuffed fish, vermin,
    and kingfishers.

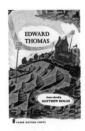

Selected Poems of Edward Thomas (2014)

9 Monday

10 Tuesday

11 Wednesday

12 Thursday

13 Friday

14 Saturday

15 Sunday

How like a winter hath my absence been

How like a winter hath my absence been
From thee, the pleasure of the fleeting year!
What freezings have I felt, what dark days seen;
What old December's bareness everywhere!
And yet this time removed was summer's time,
The teeming autumn big with rich increase,
Bearing the wanton burden of the prime,
Like widowed wombs after their lord's decease.
Yet this abundant issue seemed to me
But hope of orphans and unfathered fruit,
For summer and his pleasures wait on thee,
And, thou away, the very birds are mute,
   Or if they sing, 'tis with so dull a cheer
   That leaves look pale, dreading the winter's near.

The Map and the Clock: Poetry of Britain and Ireland Chosen by
Carol Ann Duffy and Gillian Clarke (2016)

16 Monday DAY OF RECONCILIATION (ZA)

17 Tuesday

18 Wednesday

19 Thursday

20 Friday

21 Saturday   22 Sunday

blue-screen

after Paul Verlaine

your grindr profile is an emoticon paradise
where camels and kittens go
dancing and flashing but I can tell they are :-(
beneath their primary colours

your preferences brag in arial bold
SINGLE / PASSIVE / NO STRINGS FUN
but they don't like themselves
so melt back into the blue-screen

into the silent blue-screen blank and sad
that makes the emoticons dream within their
programming and code run like teardrops
C C++ sob beneath your touchscreen

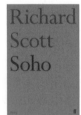

Soho (2018)

23 Monday

---

24 Tuesday CHRISTMAS EVE

---

25 Wednesday CHRISTMAS DAY (UK, IRL)

---

26 Thursday BOXING DAY/DAY OF GOODWILL/ST STEPHEN'S DAY
(UK, IRL, AUS, ZA, NZ)

---

27 Friday

---

28 Saturday   29 Sunday

Hendecasyllables

It is the very bewitching hour of eight
Which is the moment when my new day begins,
I love to hear the pretty clock striking eight
I love to get up out of my bed quickly.
Why is this? Because morning air is so cold?
Or because of new strength that seems to come then?
Both. And also because waking up ends dreams.

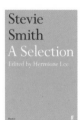

30 Monday

31 Tuesday NEW YEAR'S EVE

1 Wednesday NEW YEAR'S DAY (UK, AUS, ZA, NZ)

2 Thursday 2ND JANUARY HOLIDAY (SCT)
DAY AFTER NEW YEAR'S DAY (NZ)

3 Friday

4 Saturday 5 Sunday

A Brief Chronology of Faber's Poetry Publishing

1925 Geoffrey Faber acquires an interest in The Scientific Press and renames the firm Faber and Gwyer. ¶ The poet/bank clerk T. S. Eliot is recruited. 'What will impress my directors favourably is the sense that in you we have found a man who combines literary gifts with business instincts' – Geoffrey Faber to T. S. Eliot ¶ Eliot brought with him *The Criterion*, the quarterly periodical he had been editing since 1922. (*The Waste Land* had appeared in its first issue, brilliantly establishing its reputation.) He continued to edit it from the Faber offices until it closed in 1939. Though unprofitable, it was hugely influential, introducing early work by Auden, Empson and Spender, among others, and promoting many notable European writers, including Proust and Valéry. ¶ Publication of T. S. Eliot's *Poems, 1909–1925*, which included *The Waste Land* and a new sequence, *The Hollow Men*. ¶

1927 From 1927 to 1931 Faber publishes a series of illustrated pamphlets known as *The Ariel Poems* containing unpublished poems by an eminent poet (Thomas Hardy, W. B. Yeats, Harold Monro, Edith Sitwell and Edmund Blunden, to name but a few) along with an illustration, usually in colour, by a leading contemporary artist (including Eric Gill, Eric Ravilious, Paul Nash and Graham Sutherland). ¶

1928 Faber and Gwyer announce the *Selected Poems of Ezra Pound*, with an introduction and notes by Eliot. ¶

1929 Geoffrey Faber buys out Lady Gwyer and oversees the birth of the Faber and Faber imprint. Legend has it that Walter de la Mare, the father of Faber director Richard de la Mare, suggested the euphonious repetition: another Faber in the company name 'because you can't have too much of a good thing'. ¶

1930 W. H. Auden becomes a Faber poet with a collection entitled simply *Poems*. ¶ Eliot publishes *Ash Wednesday*. ¶

1933 Stephen Spender becomes a Faber poet with his first collection *Poems*, a companion piece to Auden's 1930 work of the same name. ¶ The first British edition of James Joyce's *Pomes Penyeach* is published. ¶

1935 The American poet Marianne Moore publishes with Faber. 'Miss Moore's poems form part of a small body of durable poetry written in our time' – T. S. Eliot ¶ Louis MacNeice becomes a Faber poet. 'The most original Irish poet of his generation' – Faber catalogue 1935 ¶

1936 The hugely influential *Faber Book of Modern Verse* (edited by Michael Roberts) is published. ¶

1937 *In Parenthesis* by David Jones is published. 'This is an epic of war. But it is like no other war-book because for the first time that experience has been reduced to "a shape in words." The impression still remains that this book is one of the most remarkable literary achievements of our time' – *Times Literary Supplement* ¶ W. H. Auden is awarded the Queen's Gold Medal for Poetry. ¶

1939 T. S. Eliot's *Old Possum's Book of Practical Cats* is published with a book jacket illustrated by the author. Originally called *Pollicle Dogs and Jellicle Cats*, the poems were written for his five godchildren. The eldest of these was Geoffrey Faber's son Tom – himself much later a director of Faber and Faber. ¶

1944 Walter de la Mare's *Peacock Pie* is published with illustrations by Edward Ardizzone. ¶

1947 Philip Larkin's first novel, *A Girl in Winter*, is published. 'A young man with an exceptionally clear sense of what, as a writer, he means to do' – *Times Literary Supplement* ¶

1948 T. S. Eliot wins the Nobel Prize in Literature. ¶

1949 Ezra Pound's *Pisan Cantos* is published. 'The most incomprehensible passages are often more stimulating than much comprehensibility which passes for poetry today' – *Times Literary Supplement* ¶

1954 *The Ariel Poems* are revived with a new set of pamphlets by W. H. Auden, Stephen Spender, Louis MacNeice, T. S. Eliot, Walter de la Mare, Cecil Day Lewis and Roy Campbell. The artists include Edward Ardizzone, Edward Bawden, Michael Ayrton and John Piper. ¶

1957 Ted Hughes comes to Faber with *The Hawk in the Rain*. ¶ Siegfried Sassoon receives the Queen's Gold Medal for Poetry. ¶

1959 Robert Lowell's collection *Life Studies* is published. ¶

1960 Saint-John Perse wins the Nobel Prize in Literature. ¶

1961 Geoffrey Faber dies. ¶ Ted Hughes's first collection of children's poems, *Meet My Folks*, is published. ¶

1963 The Geoffrey Faber Memorial Prize is established as an annual prize awarded in alternating years to a single volume of poetry or fiction by a Commonwealth author under forty. ¶

1964 Philip Larkin's *The Whitsun Weddings* is published. ¶

1965 T. S. Eliot dies. ¶ Sylvia Plath's posthumous collection, *Ariel*, is published. 'Her extraordinary achievement, poised as she was between volatile emotional state and the edge of the precipice' – Frieda Hughes ¶ Philip Larkin is awarded the Queen's Gold Medal for Poetry. ¶

1966 Seamus Heaney comes to Faber with *Death of a Naturalist*. ¶ Sylvia Plath's novel *The Bell Jar* is published by Faber. ¶

1968 Ted Hughes's *The Iron Man* is published. ¶

1971 Stephen Spender is awarded the Queen's Gold Medal for Poetry. ¶

1973 Paul Muldoon comes to Faber with his first collection, *New Weather*. ¶

1974 Ted Hughes receives the Queen's Gold Medal for Poetry. ¶

1977 Tom Paulin comes to Faber with his first collection, *A State of Justice*. ¶ Norman Nicholson receives the Queen's Gold Medal for Poetry. ¶

1980 Czesław Miłosz wins the Nobel Prize in Literature. ¶

1981 *Cats*, the Andrew Lloyd Webber musical based on *Old Possum's Book of Practical Cats*, opens in London. ¶

1984 *Rich*, a collection by Faber's own poetry editor, Craig Raine, is published. 'Puts us in touch with life as unexpectedly and joyfully as early Pasternak' – John Bayley ¶ Ted Hughes becomes Poet Laureate. ¶

1985 Douglas Dunn's collection *Elegies* is the Whitbread Book of the Year. ¶

1986 Vikram Seth's *The Golden Gate* is published. ¶

1987 Seamus Heaney's *The Haw Lantern* wins the Whitbread Poetry Award. ¶

1988 Derek Walcott is awarded the Queen's Gold Medal for Poetry. ¶

1992 Derek Walcott wins the Nobel Prize in Literature. ¶ Thom Gunn's collection *The Man with the Night Sweats* wins the Forward Poetry Prize for Best Collection, while Simon Armitage's *Kid* wins Best First Collection. ¶

1993 Andrew Motion wins the Whitbread Biography Award for his book on Philip Larkin. ¶ Don Paterson's *Nil Nil* wins the Forward Poetry Prize for Best First Collection. ¶

1994 Paul Muldoon wins the T. S. Eliot Prize for *The Annals of Chile*. ¶ Alice Oswald wins an Eric Gregory Award. ¶

1995 Seamus Heaney wins the Nobel Prize in Literature. ¶

1996 Wisława Szymborska wins the Nobel Prize in Literature. ¶ Seamus Heaney's *The Spirit Level* wins the Whitbread Book of the Year Award. 'Touched by a sense of wonder' – Blake Morrison ¶

1997 Don Paterson wins the T. S. Eliot Prize for *God's Gift to Women*. ¶ Lavinia Greenlaw wins the Forward Prize for Best Single Poem for 'A World Where News Travelled Slowly'. ¶ Ted Hughes's *Tales from Ovid* is the Whitbread Book of the Year. 'A breathtaking book' – John Carey ¶

1998 Ted Hughes wins the Whitbread Book of the Year for the second time running with *Birthday Letters*, which also wins the T. S. Eliot Prize. 'Language like lava, its molten turmoils hardening into jagged shapes' – John Carey ¶ Ted Hughes is awarded the Order of Merit. ¶ Christopher Logue receives the Wilfred Owen Poetry Award. ¶

1999 Seamus Heaney's *Beowulf* wins the Whitbread Book of the Year Award. '[Heaney is the] one living poet who can rightly claim to be Beowulf's heir' – *New York Times* ¶ A memorial service for Ted Hughes is held at Westminster Abbey. In his speech Seamus Heaney calls Hughes 'a guardian spirit of the land and language'. ¶ Hugo Williams wins the T. S. Eliot Prize for his collection *Billy's Rain*. ¶ Andrew Motion is appointed Poet Laureate. ¶

2000 Seamus Heaney receives the Wilfred Owen Poetry Award. ¶

2002 Alice Oswald wins the T. S. Eliot Prize for Poetry for her collection *Dart*. ¶

2003 Paul Muldoon is awarded the Pulitzer Prize for Poetry for *Moy Sand and Gravel*. *Landing Light* by Don Paterson wins the Whitbread Poetry Award. ¶

2004 August Kleinzahler receives the International Griffin Poetry Prize for *The Strange Hours Travellers Keep*. ¶ Hugo Williams is awarded the Queen's Gold Medal for Poetry. ¶

2005 David Harsent wins the Forward Prize for Best Collection for *Legion*. ¶ Harold Pinter receives the Wilfred Owen Poetry Award. ¶ Charles Simic receives the International Griffin Poetry Prize for *Selected Poems 1963–2003*. ¶ Nick Laird wins an Eric Gregory Award. ¶

2006 Christopher Logue wins the Whitbread Poetry Award for *Cold Calls*. ¶ The Geoffrey Faber Memorial Prize is awarded to Alice Oswald for *Woods Etc.* ¶ Seamus Heaney wins the T. S. Eliot Prize for *District and Circle*. ¶

2007 Tony Harrison is awarded the Wilfred Owen Poetry Award. ¶ Daljit Nagra wins the Forward Prize for Best First Collection for *Look We Have Coming to Dover!* ¶ James Fenton receives the Queen's Gold Medal for Poetry. ¶

2008 Daljit Nagra wins the South Bank Show / Arts Council Decibel Award. ¶ Mick Imlah's collection *The Lost Leader* wins the Forward Prize for Best Collection. ¶

2009 Carol Ann Duffy becomes Poet Laureate. ¶ Don Paterson's *Rain* wins the Forward Poetry Prize for Best Collection, while *The Striped World* by Emma Jones wins the Best First Collection Prize. ¶

2010 *The Song of Lunch* by Christopher Reid is shortlisted for the Ted Hughes Award for New Work in Poetry and he is awarded the Costa Poetry Award for *A Scattering*. ¶ The John Florio Prize for Italian Translation 2010 is awarded to Jamie McKendrick for *The Embrace*. ¶ Derek Walcott wins both the Warwick Prize and the T. S. Eliot Prize for Poetry for his collection *White Egrets*. ¶ *Rain* by Don Paterson is shortlisted for the Saltire Scottish Book of the Year. ¶ Tony Harrison is awarded the Prix Européen de Littérature. ¶ The Keats–Shelley Prize is awarded to Simon Armitage for his poem 'The Present'. ¶ The Forward Prize for Best Collection is awarded to Seamus Heaney for *Human Chain*. ¶ Also shortlisted for the Forward Prize for Best Collection are Lachlan Mackinnon for *Small Hours* and Jo Shapcott for *Of Mutability*. ¶ The Centre for Literacy in Primary Education (CLPE) Poetry Prize is awarded to Carol Ann Duffy for *New and Collected Poems for Children*. ¶ Alice Oswald wins the Ted Hughes Award for New Work in Poetry for *Weeds and Wild Flowers*. ¶ *The Striped World* by Emma Jones is shortlisted for the Adelaide Festival Poetry Award. ¶ The Queen's Gold Medal for Poetry is awarded to Don Paterson. ¶

2011 *Of Mutability* by Jo Shapcott is the Costa Book of the Year. ¶ *Human Chain* by Seamus Heaney and *Maggot* by Paul Muldoon are both shortlisted for the *Irish Times* Poetry Now Award. ¶ *Night* by David Harsent is shortlisted for the Forward Prize for Best Collection. ¶ 'Bees' by Jo Shapcott is shortlisted for the Forward Prize for Best Single Poem. ¶ A new digital edition of T. S. Eliot's *The Waste Land* for iPad is launched, bringing to life one of the most revolutionary poems of the last hundred years, illuminated by a wealth of interactive features. ¶ The Queen's Gold Medal for Poetry is awarded to Jo Shapcott. ¶ At Westminster Abbey a memorial is dedicated to Ted Hughes in Poets' Corner. ¶

2012 *The Death of King Arthur* by Simon Armitage is shortlisted for the T. S. Eliot Prize. ¶ *The World's Two Smallest Humans* by Julia Copus is shortlisted for the T. S. Eliot Prize and the Costa Poetry Award. ¶ David Harsent's collection *Night* wins the International Griffin Poetry Prize. ¶ *81 Austerities* by Sam Riviere wins the Felix Dennis Prize for Best First Collection, one of the Forward Prizes for Poetry. ¶ *Farmers Cross* by Bernard O'Donoghue is shortlisted for the *Irish Times* Poetry Now Award. ¶

2013 The Forward Prize for Best First Collection is awarded to Emily Berry for *Dear Boy*. ¶ Hugo Williams is shortlisted for the Forward Prize for Best Single

Poem for 'From the Dialysis Ward'. ¶ Alice Oswald is awarded the Warwick Prize for Writing for her collection *Memorial*, which also wins the Poetry Society's Corneliu M. Popescu Prize for poetry in translation. ¶ The Queen's Gold Medal for Poetry is awarded to Douglas Dunn. ¶ The shortlist for the T. S. Eliot Prize includes Daljit Nagra for *The Ramayana: A Retelling* and Maurice Riordan for *The Water Stealer*. ¶ *Pink Mist* by Owen Sheers wins the Hay Festival Medal for Poetry. ¶ In his eulogy for Seamus Heaney, Paul Muldoon says, 'We remember the beauty of Seamus Heaney – as a bard, and in his being.' In November the first official tribute evenings to Heaney are held at Harvard, then in New York, followed by events at the Royal Festival Hall in London, the Waterfront Hall, Belfast, and the Sheldonian, Oxford. ¶

2014 Maurice Riordan is shortlisted for the Pigott Poetry Prize for *The Water Stealer*. ¶ Hugo Williams is shortlisted for the Forward Prize for Best Collection for *I Knew the Bride*. ¶ Daljit Nagra is awarded the Society of Authors Travelling Scholarship. ¶ Nick Laird's *Go Giants* is shortlisted for the *Irish Times* Poetry Now Award. ¶ Emily Berry, Emma Jones and Daljit Nagra are announced as three of the Poetry Book Society's Next Generation Poets 2014. ¶ *Pink Mist* by Owen Sheers is named the Wales Book of the Year after winning the poetry category. ¶

2015 *Fire Songs* by David Harsent is awarded the T. S. Eliot Prize for Poetry. ¶ Alice Oswald wins the Ted Hughes Award for New Work for *Tithonus*, a poem and performance commissioned by London's Southbank Centre. ¶ *One Thousand Things Worth Knowing* by Paul Muldoon wins the Pigott Poetry Prize. ¶ Don Paterson is awarded the Neustadt International Prize for Literature. ¶ *Terror* by Toby Martinez de las Rivas is shortlisted for the Seamus Heaney Centre for Poetry's Prize for First Full Collection. ¶ Paul Muldoon's *One Thousand Things Worth Knowing* is shortlisted for the Forward Prize for Best Collection. ¶ James Fenton is awarded the Pen Pinter Prize. ¶ *40 Sonnets* by Don Paterson wins the Costa Poetry Award, and is shortlisted for the T. S. Eliot Prize. ¶

2016 Don Paterson is shortlisted for the International Griffin Poetry Prize. ¶ *40 Sonnets* by Don Paterson is shortlisted for the Saltire Society Literary Awards. ¶ *The Seasons of Cullen Church* by Bernard O'Donoghue is shortlisted for the T. S. Eliot Prize. ¶ Jack Underwood receives a Somerset Maugham Award. ¶ An excerpt from *Salt* by David Harsent is shortlisted for the Forward Prize for Best Single Poem. ¶

2017 *The Unaccompanied* by Simon Armitage, *Stranger, Baby* by Emily Berry and *The Noise of a Fly* by Douglas Dunn all receive Recommendations from the Poetry Book Society. They also give a Special Commendation to *Selected Poems of Thom*

Gunn, edited by Clive Wilmer. ¶ Simon Armitage receives the PEN Award for Poetry in Translation for *Pearl*. ¶ Bernard O'Donoghue's collection *The Seasons of Cullen Church* is shortlisted for the Pigott Poetry Prize. ¶ Emily Berry's collection *Stranger, Baby* is shortlisted for the Forward Prize for Best Collection. ¶ Sam Riviere's collection *Kim Kardashian's Marriage* is shortlisted for the Ledbury Poetry Prize. ¶ Douglas Dunn's collection *The Noise of a Fly* is shortlisted for the T. S. Eliot Prize. ¶ Paul Muldoon is awarded the Queen's Gold Medal for Poetry. ¶

2018 Matthew Francis's collection *The Mabinogi* is shortlisted for the Ted Hughes Award and Welsh Book of the Year. ¶ Toby Martinez de las Rivas's collection *Black Sun* is shortlisted for the Forward Prize for Best Collection. ¶ Richard Scott's collection *Soho* is shortlisted for the Forward Prize for Best First Collection, the T. S. Eliot Prize and the Costa Poetry Award. ¶ Owen Sheers is the recipient of the Wilfred Owen Poetry Award for 2018. ¶ Daljit Nagra receives a Society of Authors Cholmondeley Award. ¶ Seamus Heaney's collection *100 Poems* is shortlisted for the 2018 Books Are My Bag Readers Awards, Poetry category. ¶ Nick Laird's collection *Feel Free* is shortlisted for the T. S. Eliot Prize. ¶ Zaffar Kunial's collection *Us* is shortlisted for the Costa Poetry Award and the T. S. Eliot Prize. ¶ Hannah Sullivan's collection *Three Poems* is shortlisted for the Roehampton Poetry Prize and the Costa Poetry Award, and goes on to win the T. S. Eliot Prize. ¶ Simon Armitage is awarded the Queen's Gold Medal for Poetry. ¶

2019 Simon Armitage is appointed Poet Laureate. ¶ Richard Scott's collection *Soho* is shortlisted for the Roehampton Poetry Prize and the Polari First Book Prize. ¶ Hannah Sullivan's collection *Three Poems* wins the John Pollard Foundation International Poetry Prize and is shortlisted for the Ted Hughes Award, the Seamus Heaney First Collection Prize and the Michael Murphy Memorial Prize. ¶ Sophie Collins's collection *Who Is Mary Sue?* is shortlisted for the 2018 Saltire Society's Scottish Poetry Book of the Year and wins both the Michael Murphy Memorial Prize and an Eric Gregory Award. ¶ Ishion Hutchinson's collection *House of Lords and Commons* wins the Windham-Campbell Prize. ¶ Lavinia Greenlaw's collection *The Built Moment* is shortlisted for the Roehampton Poetry Prize and the East Anglian Book Award (poetry category). ¶ Zaffar Kunial's collection *Us* is shortlisted for the 2019 Rathbones Folio Prize, the Roehampton Poetry Prize and the Michael Murphy Memorial Prize. ¶ 'The Window' from Mary Jean Chan's collection *Flèche* is shortlisted for the Forward Prize for Best Single Poem and her poem 'The Fencer' wins the Geoffrey Dearmer Prize. ¶ Poems from Rachael Allen, Lavinia Greenlaw, Paul Muldoon and Hugo Williams are Highly Commended for the Forward Prizes for Poetry. ¶ Ilya

Kaminsky's collection *Deaf Republic* is shortlisted for the Forward Prize for Best Collection, the T. S. Eliot Prize and the US National Book Award (poetry category). ¶

2020 Mary Jean Chan's collection *Flèche* wins the Costa Poetry Award and is shortlisted for both the John Pollard International Poetry Prize and the Seamus Heaney First Collection Poetry Prize. ¶ Nick Laird's collection *Feel Free* is shortlisted for the Derek Walcott Poetry Prize. ¶ Julia Copus's collection *Girlhood* is shortlisted for the Derek Walcott Poetry Prize. ¶ Paul Muldoon's collection *Frolic and Detour* is shortlisted for the *Irish Times* Poetry Now Award. ¶ Natalie Diaz's collection *Postcolonial Love Poem* is shortlisted for the T. S. Eliot Prize and the US National Book Award (poetry category). ¶

2021 Natalie Diaz's collection *Postcolonial Love Poem* wins the Pulitzer Prize for Poetry, is a finalist for the Neustadt International Prize for Literature and *LA Times* Prize for Poetry, and is longlisted for the Laurel Prize. ¶ Jack Underwood's collection *A Year in the New Life* is shortlisted for the T. S. Eliot Prize. ¶ Barbara Kingsolver's collection *How to Fly* is longlisted for the Laurel Prize. ¶ Mary Jean Chan's collection *Flèche* is a finalist for the LAMBDA Award for Lesbian Poetry. ¶ The Derek Walcott Prize for Poetry shortlist includes Simon Armitage's collection *Magnetic Field*; David Harsent's collection *Loss*;

Andrew Motion's collection *Randomly Moving Particles*; Don Paterson's collection *Zonal*; and Christopher Reid's collection *The Late Sun*. ¶ Maurice Riordan's collection *Shoulder Tap* is shortlisted for the Pigott Poetry Prize. ¶ Paul Muldoon's collection *Howdie-Skelp* is shortlisted for the Pigott Poetry Prize. ¶

2022 Nidhi Zak/Aria Eipe's collection *Auguries of a Minor God* is shortlisted for the John Pollard Prize and the Dylan Thomas Prize. ¶ Jack Underwood's collection *A Year in the New Life* and Emily Berry's collection *Unexhausted Time* are longlisted for the Laurel Prize. ¶ Zaffar Kunial's collection *England's Green* is shortlisted for the T. S. Eliot Prize. ¶ Victoria Adukwei Bulley's collection *Quiet* is shortlisted for the T. S. Eliot Prize. ¶ 'Up Late' by Nick Laird is shortlisted for the Forward Prize for Best Single Poem. ¶ Simon Armitage's collection *The Owl and the Nightingale* is shortlisted for the Derek Walcott Prize. ¶

Acknowledgements

Poetry

'The Skylight' from 'Glanmore Sonnets', taken from *Seeing Things* © The Estate of Seamus Heaney ¶ 'Sheep in Fog' taken from *Sylvia Plath Poems Chosen by Carol Ann Duffy* © The Estate of Sylvia Plath ¶ 'Hadrian's Wall' taken from *British Museum* © Daljit Nagra ¶ '(It was as if I were asleep)' taken from *Unexhausted Time* © Emily Berry ¶ 'Heart for Sale' taken from *Never Good with Horses* © Simon Armitage ¶ 'Gwawrddur [99]' taken from *The Gododdin* © Gillian Clarke ¶ 'Usk' from 'Landscapes III' taken from *The Poems of T.S. Eliot Volume One* © Set Copyrights Limited ¶ 'The Pan' taken from *Collected Poems* © The Estate of Ted Hughes ¶ 'There You Are' taken from *Quiet* © Victoria Adukwei Bulley ¶ 'Foxglove Country' taken from *England's Green* © Zaffar Kunial ¶ 'The Question' taken from *Living Weapon* © Rowan Ricardo Phillips ¶ 'North European' taken from *The Missing Months* © Lachlan Mackinnon ¶ 'Mere' taken from *Wing* © Matthew Francis ¶ 'By the River' taken from *Anecdotal Evidence* © Wendy Cope ¶ 'The fishermen rowing homeward . . .' taken from *The Poetry of Derek Walcott 1948–2013* © The Estate of Derek Walcott ¶ 'Dayroom' taken from *Girlhood* © Julia Copus ¶ 'Conversation with Fantasy Mother' taken from *Flèche* © Mary Jean Chan ¶ 'A Toast' taken from *Dancing in Odessa* © Ilya Kaminsky ¶ 'Fog' taken from *Toys/Tricks/Traps* © Christopher Reid ¶ Extract from *God Complex* © Rachael Allen ¶ 'The Mud Sermon' taken from *School of Instructions* © Ishion Hutchinson ¶ 'A Winter Apple' taken from *The Arctic* © Don Paterson ¶ 'blue-screen' taken from *Soho* © Richard Scott ¶ 'Hendecasyllables' taken from *Stevie Smith: A Selection* © The Estate of Stevie Smith

All poetry reprinted by permission of Faber & Faber unless otherwise stated.

Picture credits

Go Giants by Nick Laird, design by Faber, series design by Pentagram

Love by Walter de la Mare, design by Barnett Freedman

Solstices by Louis MacNeice, design by Berthold Wolpe

A Vertical Art by Simon Armitage, design by Luke Bird

Collected Poems by W. H. Auden, design by Faber, series design by Pentagram

Dante's Drum-Kit by Douglas Dunn, design by Faber, illustration: Etching of Arachne from 12th Canto of Dante's 'Purgatory' by Gustave Doré (1832–83). Private Collection/Bridgeman Art Library

The Sense of Movement by Thom Gunn, design by Berthold Wolpe

The Gododdin by Gillian Clarke, design by Faber, image © Nik Keevil / Shutterstock

NOTES

Simon Armitage
Book of Matches

Simon Armitage
Seeing Stars

W. H. Auden
The Dyer's Hand

W. H. Auden
Selected Poems
Revised Edition
Edited by Edward Mendels

Mark Ford
Soft Sift

Matthew Francis
Muscovy

Lavinia Greenlaw
The Casual Perfect

Ian Hamilton
Collected Poems
Edited by Alan Jenkins

James Joyce
Poems and Shorter Writings
Edited by Richard Ellmann
A. Walton Litz and
John Whittier-Ferguson

Nick Laird
Go Giants

Logue's Homer
Cold Calls
War Music continued

Andrew Motion
The Cinder Path

Don Paterson
Selected Poems

Sylvia Plath
Ariel

Ezra Pound
Selected Poems
1908–1969

Christopher Reid
Nonsense